865

To Jack Michael

First published in Great Britain in 1998 by
Frances Lincoln Limited, 4 Torriano Mews
Torriano Avenue, London NW5 2RZ

First paperback edition 1999

The author and publishers would like to thank Stephen Hall of the
Southampton Oceanography Centre for his help.

British Library Cataloguing in Publication Data
available on request

ISBN 0-7112-1213-9 hardback
      0-7112-1214-7 paperback

Printed in Hong Kong

9 8 7 6 5 4 3 2 1

The Deep Blue Sea

AN OCEAN WILDLIFE BOOK

Jakki Wood

FRANCES LINCOLN

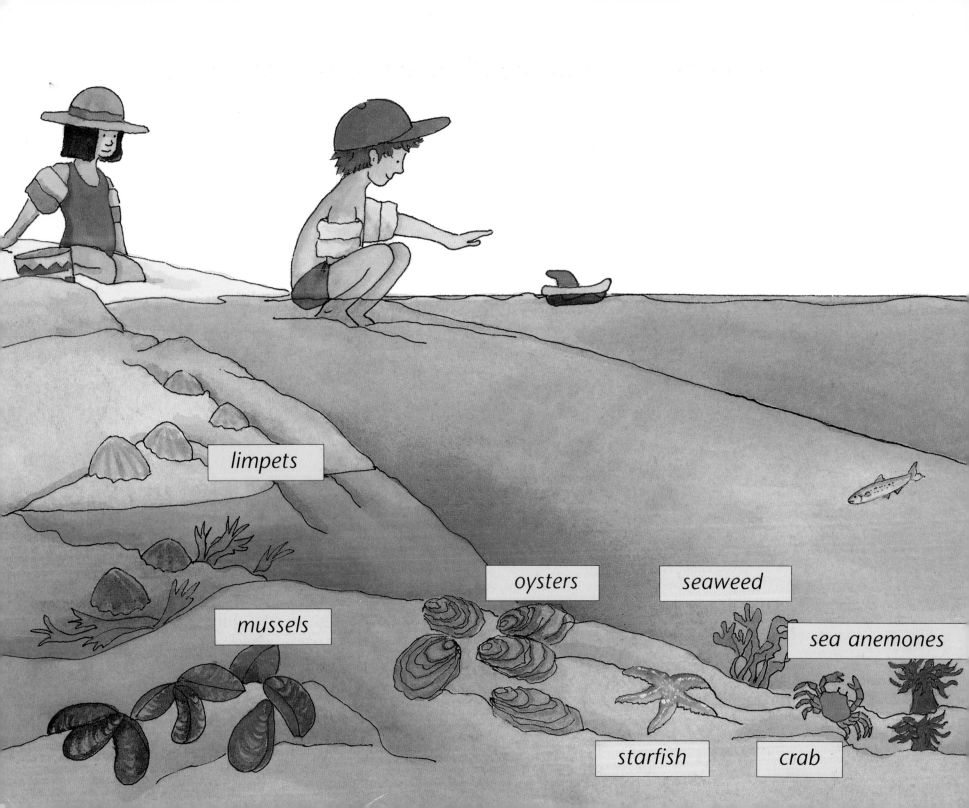

limpets

oysters

seaweed

mussels

sea anemones

starfish

crab

On the beach in California, Tom gives his boat a *push!*

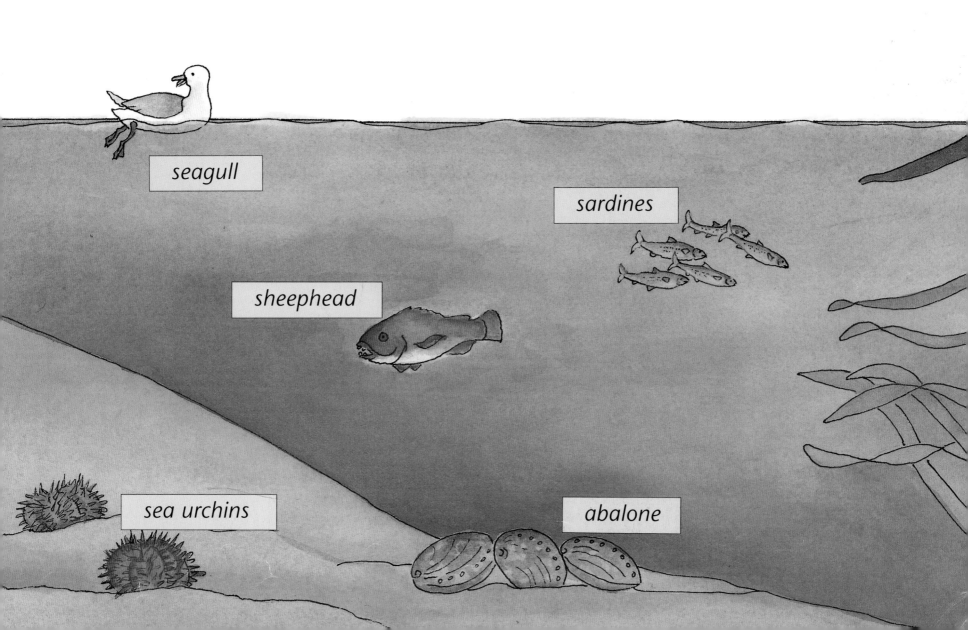

It drifts away on the ocean currents.

sea kelp forest

sea lion

sea otter

sea snail

brown pelican

anchovies

Out in the Pacific, killer whales play with Tom's boat ...

tuna

but they don't break it.

Pacific salmon

killer whale

thresher shark

Splash! Flying fish leap and glide.

flying fish

grey whale

octopus

black smoker

Tom's boat is just north of Australia,
near a tiny coral island.

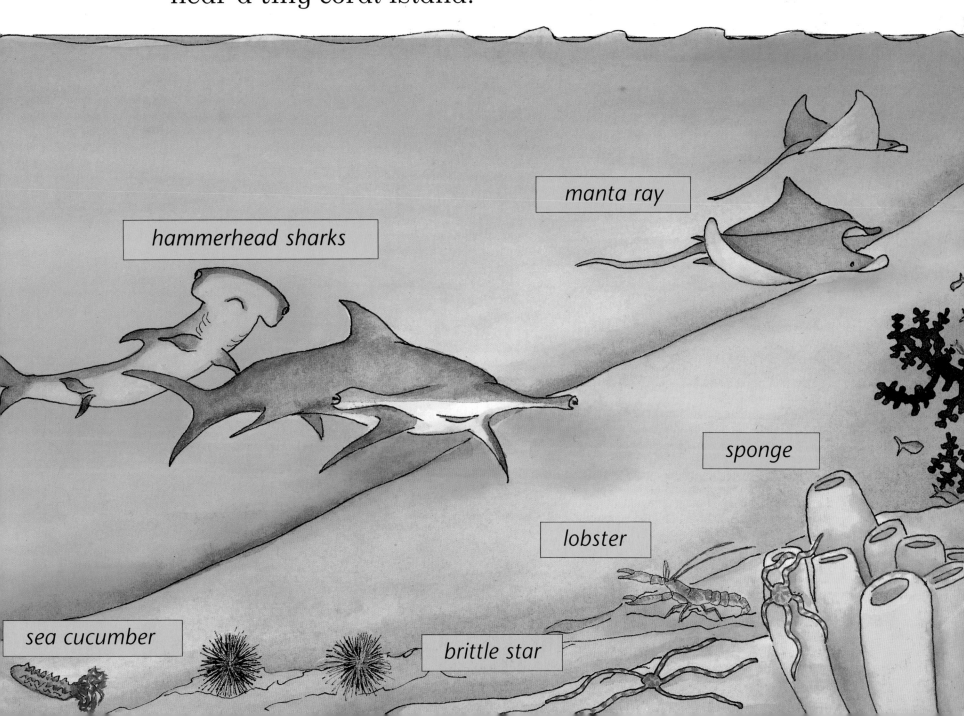

manta ray

hammerhead sharks

sponge

lobster

sea cucumber

brittle star

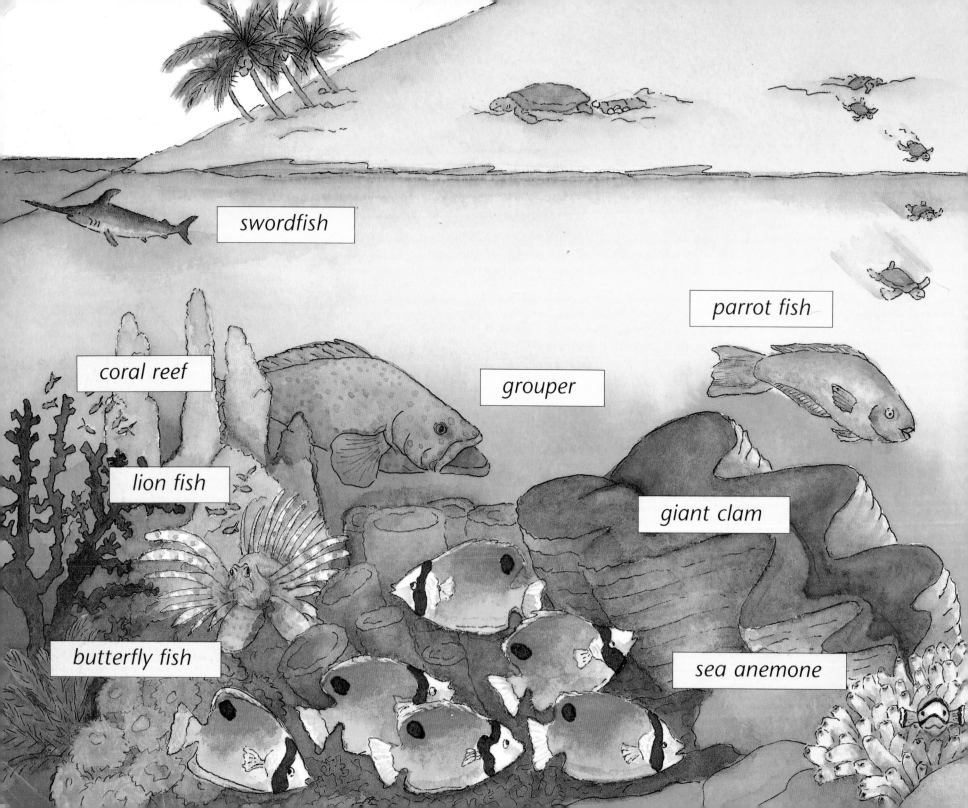

swordfish

parrot fish

coral reef

grouper

lion fish

giant clam

butterfly fish

sea anemone

A friendly turtle gives the boat a ride.

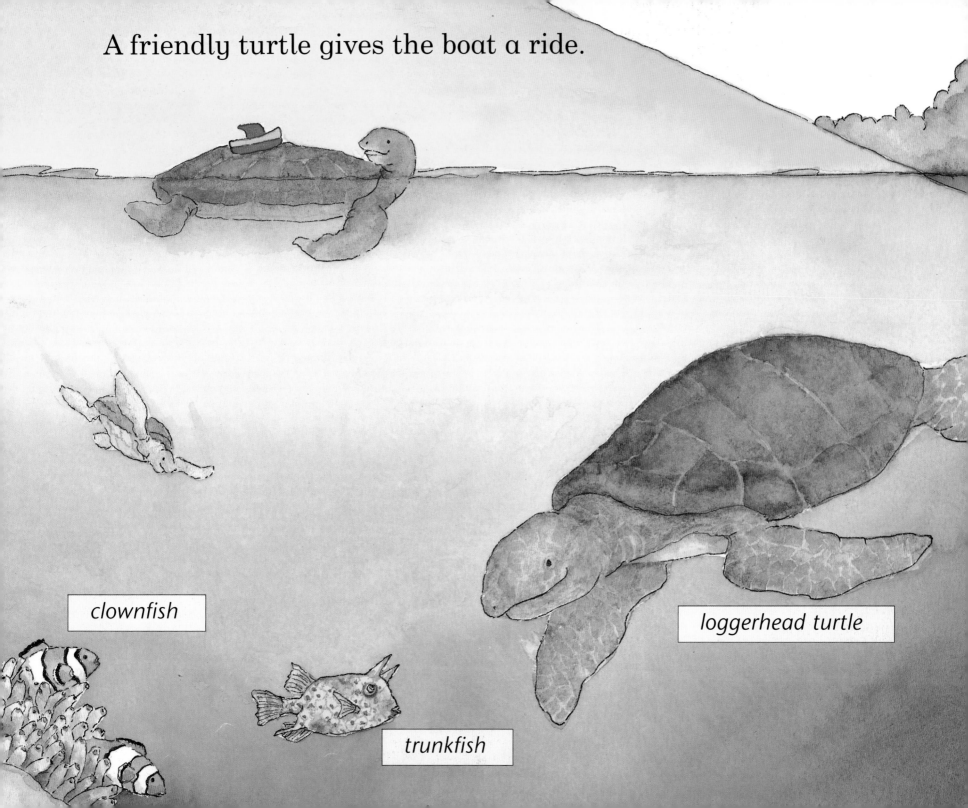

clownfish

trunkfish

loggerhead turtle

In the Indian Ocean, a great storm blows up.

scad

Fish swim calmly beneath the waves.

Safe from the storm, south of Africa,
the boat is noticed by some curious penguins ...

krill

Southern fur seal

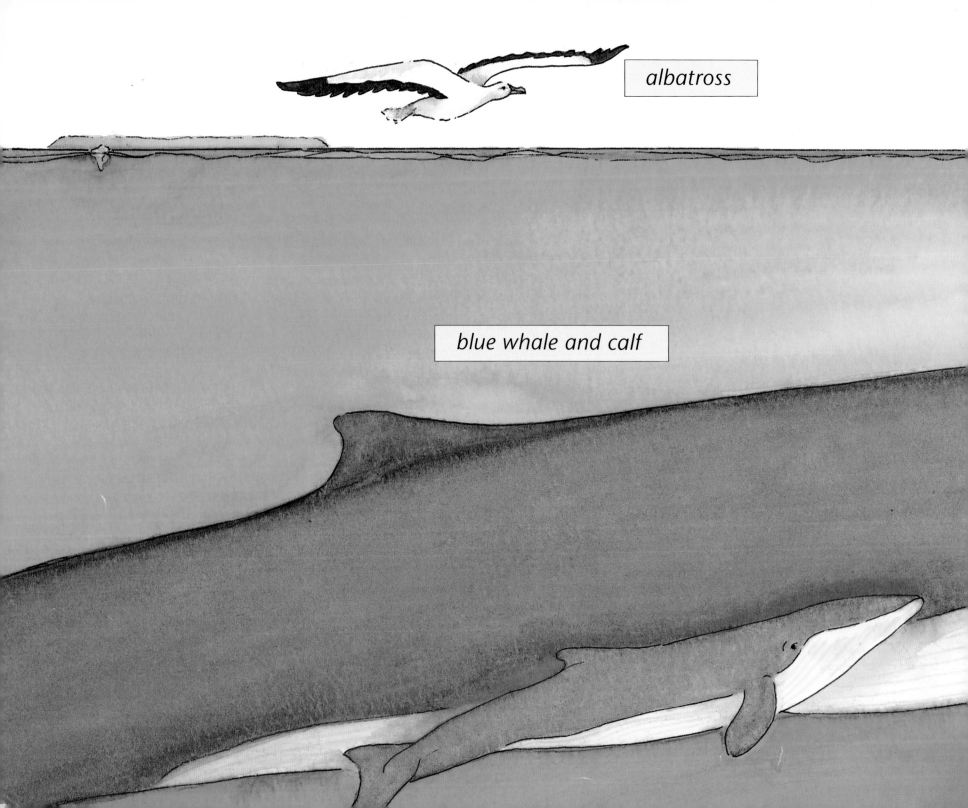

albatross

blue whale and calf

and watched by a huge blue whale.

Tom's boat has reached the Atlantic Ocean.

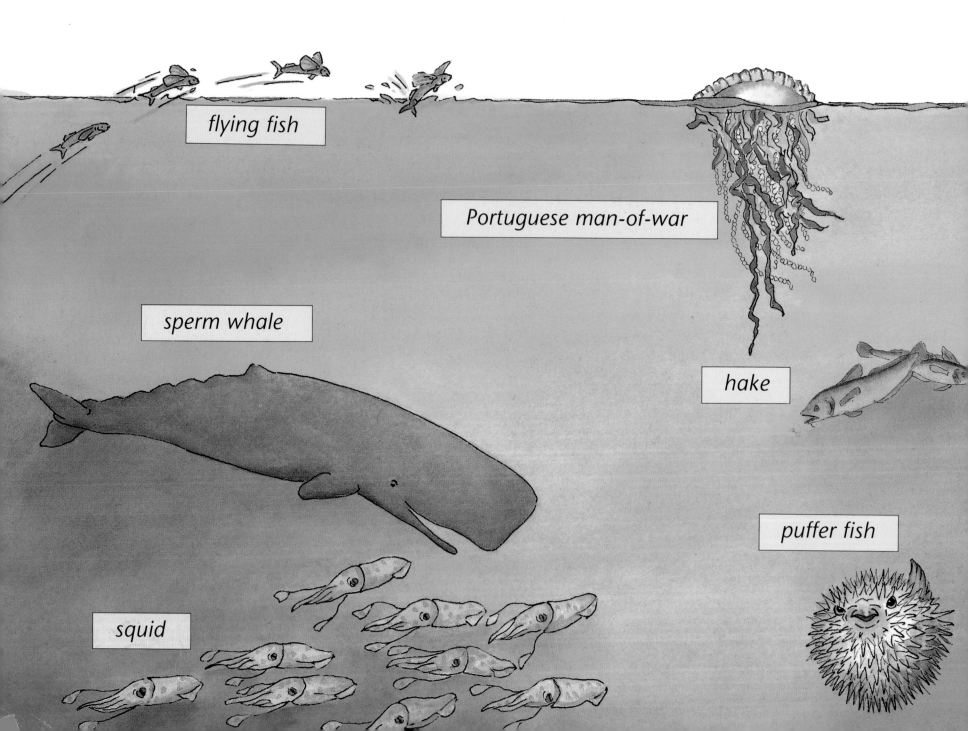

flying fish

Portuguese man-of-war

sperm whale

hake

squid

puffer fish

The dolphins would like to keep it.

common dolphin

But the warm current carries it above the wreck of a pirate ship ...

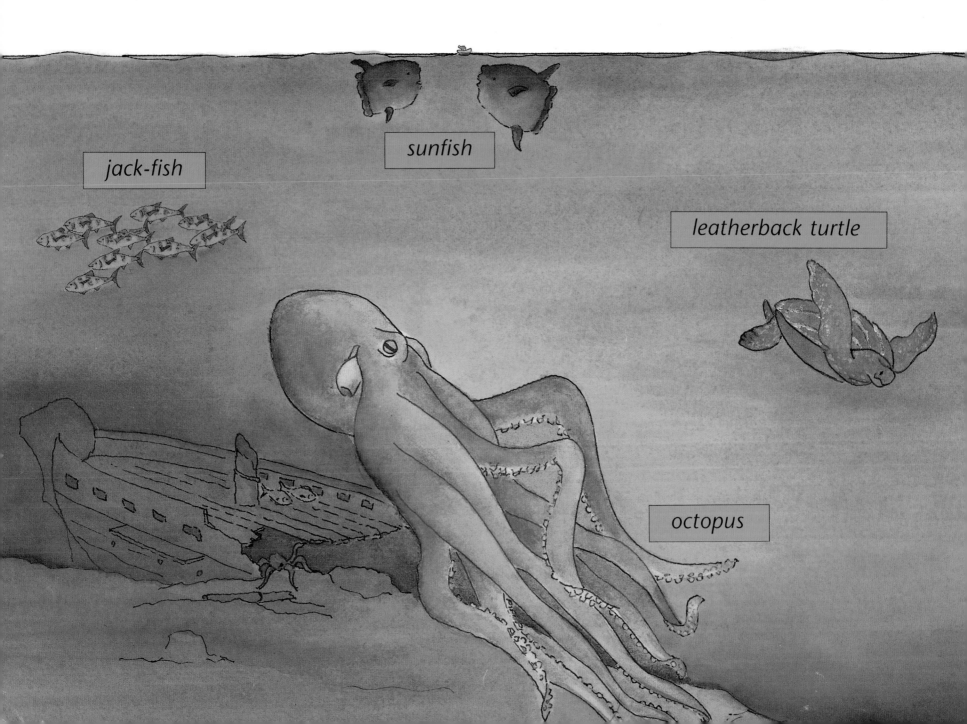

sunfish

jack-fish

leatherback turtle

octopus

through the Sargasso Sea ...

sargassum weed

sailfish

eel

and right across the Atlantic Ocean.

porbeagle shark

hatchet fish

angler fish

gulper eel

Far, far below, strange creatures swim in the dark water.

squid

black smoker

At last Tom's boat is close to land again.

cormorant

herring

A dolphin pushes it towards the shore.

bottlenose dolphin

pilot whale

A boy reaches into the water,
and grabs the red-and-yellow boat.

seagull

puffin

stingray

grey seal

cod

John Dory

Tom's boat has drifted all the way to Britain.
Now someone else will play with it.

mackerel

crab

plaice

cockles

Can you follow the little boat's journey? The blue line shows the route it takes, drifting with the wind and the ocean currents.

Look at some of the fish and other sea creatures on the map. They will help you to match areas of the map to the story inside. Follow the arrows from California on the western coast of the USA, to Cornwall in southwest England – a sea journey of more than 40,000 kilometres.

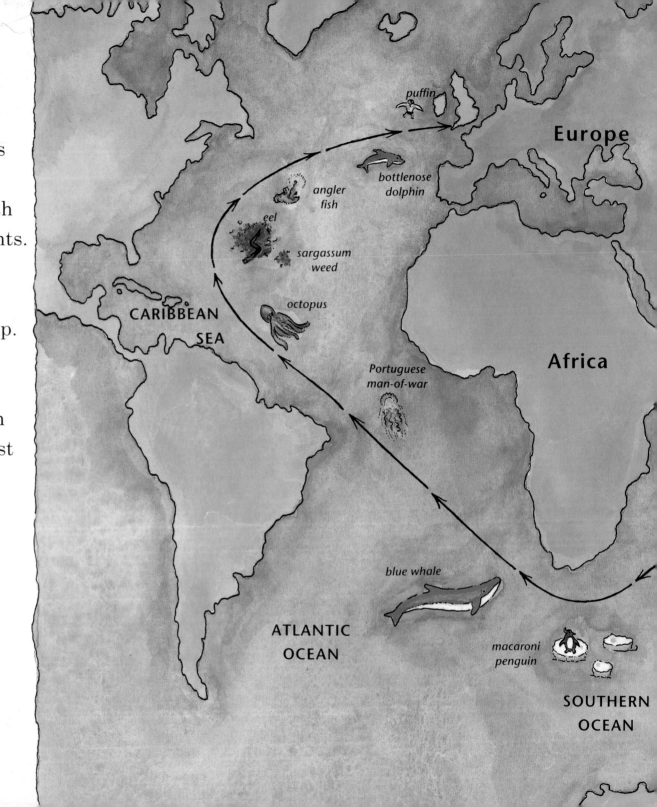

puffin

Europe

bottlenose dolphin

angler fish

eel

sargassum weed

octopus

CARIBBEAN SEA

Africa

Portuguese man-of-war

blue whale

ATLANTIC OCEAN

macaroni penguin

SOUTHERN OCEAN

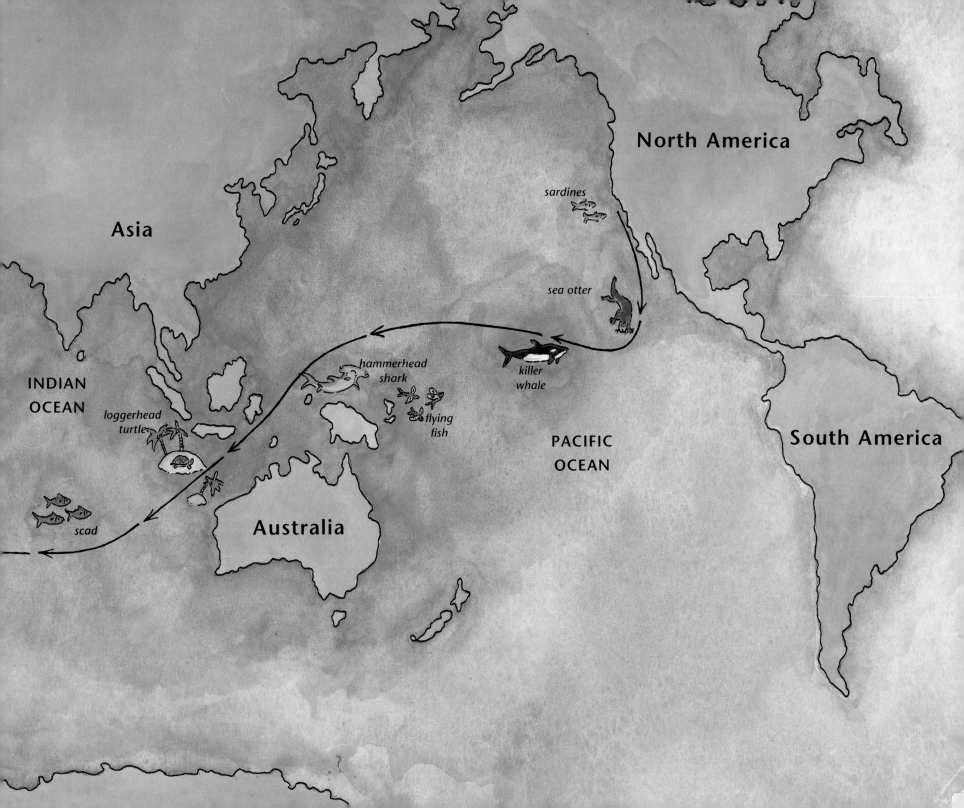

North America

Asia

sardines

sea otter

INDIAN
OCEAN

hammerhead
shark

killer
whale

loggerhead
turtle

flying
fish

PACIFIC
OCEAN

South America

scad

Australia